CONTENTS

CURRICULUM LINKS

There's **so much more** to this fabulous collection of songs than just the music and lyrics. Get the most out of them by exploring some of the ways you can **link their content to wider areas of the curriculum.**

To help you **unpack their potential** in this way, we've given you a head start with suggestions here, linking to particular songs where relevant.

BIG band

DESIGN & TECHNOLOGY

🎵 **SONG:** Take 5 Styles / Take A Major Scale

In music an enormous range of melodies and harmonies can be derived from just one familiar set of notes. In the same way, different recipes that all use one similar ingredient can create a huge variety of culinary delights. Get the children to list their **five favourite recipes that involve using an egg.** These could include omelettes, pasta, pancakes, cakes or meringues. Try investigating international dishes such as frittata, rosti, empanadas or Thai fish cakes.

🎵 **SONG:** New Day Blues / Just Sing!

Make a 'Doodle video' using video software like Windows Movie Maker or Apple VideoPad for Macs. Choose a song to learn as a class. Number each line of the song then put the number and the lyric line on the back of pieces of A4 paper. Get children to draw a picture showing the meaning of the song line in pairs and when finished, take photos of each picture to create the class Doodle video!

HISTORY

Research the tradition of singing at football matches and why football chants are considered one of the last remaining sources of an oral folk song tradition in the United Kingdom. Where did it start and what styles of music and songs do the crowds sing, such as When The Saints Go Marching In or Knees Up Mother Brown?

MATHS M=a+3

🎵 **SONG:** It's Nearly Playtime

Ask the children to draw a chart showing the breakdown of their day. How much of their day do they spend at school, and when they are there how much time is spent on lessons and how much is spent playing? How long do they spend asleep, or watching TV?!

🎵 **SONG:** Just Sing! / Sing Anyway

Conduct a class/school survey, to find out when or where people sing most (include school staff as well), e.g. I sing most in the... kitchen/bath/car/school; when I'm happy/sad/excited etc.

ART

🎵 SONG: Take 5 Styles

Try this exercise of **painting with sound** by tying bells to the end of the children's paintbrushes! Take some loose jingle bells, pipe cleaners, paper and paint. Thread the bells on to the pipe cleaners and wrap around the paintbrushes (thick-handled brushes will work best). Let the children explore and shake the bell-brushes before they have paint on them! Discuss all the different sounds that are made by using different brush strokes and see how artistically inspired the children can get by the sounds they are making.

🎵 SONG: Sun Arise

Abstract art and its style demonstrate a departure from reality in art. The artist Wassily Kandinsky, himself a musician, was inspired by the possibility of the shapes and colour in his paintings being influenced by, and taking shape while listening to, music. Show his painting *Black Lines no. 189* pointing out some examples of the abstract art techniques used such as:

Linear strokes – horizontal or vertical lines

Cross-hatching – closely spaced parallel lines applied at different angles to create different textures and darker tones

Feathering – colour blended out towards the edges

Scumbling – broken, speckled, scratchy colours layered over each other

Pointillism – small, distinct dots of pure colour applied in patterns to form an image

Ask the children to listen to a piece of music (perhaps *Sun Arise*) and create their own abstract painting, applying some of the techniques used by Kandinsky.

You could also reverse this process: plan a lesson where the children try to interpret the *Black Lines no. 189* using sounds and instruments to represent the different images in the painting, such as linear strokes and feathering.

R.E.

🎵 SONG: Thank You Lord

Corporate prayers are often written in a repetitive way so that they focus the mind and are easy to remember. Listen to the Taize song '*Nada Te Turbe*' on the Internet. A Spanish chant is repeated all the way through while soloists sing individual prayers periodically:

Nothing can harm you, nothing can frighten.
God's love is always there.
Nothing can harm you, nothing can frighten.
Trust in Him always.

Agree a theme of prayer with the children and a phrase that can be repeated by the whole group after different individual prayers such as 'God's love is always there'. Get the children to write short prayers with a partner to read aloud. Finish each prayer with an 'Amen', then everyone says the communal phrase together before the next prayer is read aloud.

♪ SONG: Take 5 Styles / If You Can Walk, You Can Dance

Practise some different styles of dance from around the world, which can be done with a partner or group. You will need some space to stand in a line or find a dance partner.

Try these simple suggestions to include in your choreography:

Samba – use a quick 'step, ball, change' step: start with the feet together, take the right foot back, do a little step on the ball of the left foot then bring the right foot back to the original position. Repeat, this time stepping back on the left foot. Add some hip action for an authentic samba feel. It's fast and fun!

Swing – to a swinging side-to-side step movement, add a finger click to the second and fourth beats of the bar and groove to the beat.

Waltz – for a graceful waltz step, use a slower 'step, ball, change' action on each of the '1, 2, 3' beats of the bar. Or, if you're up for a challenge, ask partners to glide in circles.

Tango – a fun partner dance. As each couple holds hands, make sure one arm from each pair is straight out to the front. Take long steps on beat one followed by two quick steps on beats three and four. Add a strong flick of the head for some Tango attitude!

Israeli – for this group dance, link arms taking three steps to the side with alternating feet, finishing off with a kick on the fourth beat to add flair to your Israeli dance.

P.S.H.E.

♪ SONG: It's Nearly Playtime

Playing well together is important – whether in the playground or playing music! Try playing this game of trust, communication and teamwork. Take some wool or rope to tie at different heights in a large play area. Divide the group into two and give each team a blindfold. One pair from each team enters the 'spider web'. The sighted player must guide their blindfolded partner by directing her or him through the spider web to the other side. S/he can only guide with vocal directions, no touching. The team with the fastest time wins the game.

♪ SONG: Sing Anyway / I Have A Song To Sing

Hold a sponsored 'sing-along' to raise money for a charity. Each class could choose a programme of favourite songs to sing. How many would you need to fill an afternoon, or even a whole day?! You could also include some smaller choirs or a few soloists.

How about starting a whole school choir? Include staff as well as pupils. You could even open your choir up to the local community and invite parents and friends to join in.

♪ SONG: We Are One

What makes a singing school? Discuss how singing can improve the school day by including it in celebrations, fact-learning, expressing emotions, feeling good, energizing etc.

GEOGRAPHY

♫ SONG: New Day Blues

'The Blues' is the name given to the style of music created by African-Americans at the end of the 19th century in southern USA. They combined African melodies and rhythms with a more Western European musical structure. Research where the first African-Americans came from and why they were 'singing the blues'. Draw a map of the journey of the first slaves from Africa to America; include details of the differences between the countries, the ocean covered and weather conditions etc.

♫ SONG: Take 5 Styles

Use a map-of-the-world template for the children to research, draw and describe different types of music played by people on all the different continents. Split the class into small groups and assign each a different continent in order to create an impressive whole-class display. To support this activity take a look at Marbles the Brain Store's music video *Tour the World*, available on YouTube.

SCIENCE

Sound waves are vibrations, which move through different media such as air and water before reaching our ears. Find out how small sounds can still make a big noise by using a sound conductor: blow up a balloon and hold it close to your ear while you tap lightly on the other side. Write down the results of your experiment. What happened? (*Blowing up the balloon forced the air molecules inside it closer together, which means they were better able to conduct the sound waves than the air around the balloon.*)

♫ SONG: I Have A Song To Sing / Just Sing! / New Day Blues

Study the health benefits of singing by drawing a map of the body illustrating the following areas:

The physical act of singing releases endorphins – the brain's 'feel good' chemicals

Group-singing creates a sense of belonging and connection

Singing exercises core muscles and encourages oxygen intake, which leads to increased alertness

Singing is a natural stress-reducer

Singing even improves neurological functioning

ENGLISH

Ask the children to assign musical characteristics to well-known characters from books they know. List some of the children's favourite characters, such as Toad from *Wind in the Willows* or Baloo from *The Jungle Book*. Ask each group to describe a different character as if they were being expressed in music. Which instruments would best represent the characters? What about rhythms, dynamics or tempo? Get groups to feedback their descriptions to the class explaining how they came to their decisions. Why not try performing a soundscape where the children can use instruments to produce the sounds they imagined for their particular characters?

♫ SONG: Take 5 Styles

Listen to a piece of music and start to write down words that come to mind. These could be colours, emotions, places or any other describing words. Next, write a poem using your list of words. Read through *When I Heard The Music* by Pie Corbett for inspiration; it uses lots of similes and metaphors to describe how the music transports the writer to different places and memories. What other types of literary devices or styles could be used for the poems? Ballad, acrostic, Cinquain, haiku, rhyming couplet?

SONG INFORMATION  at a glance

Song	Song summary	Age	Subject	Musical style
If You Can Walk, You Can Dance	Inspired by a Zimbabwean proverb, this upbeat, lively song promotes a positive outlook and encourages a 'have-a-go' attitude to singing, dancing and to living.	5+	PE; Health; Dance	Funky & energetic!
We're Here Again	An inclusive, 'feel-good' song celebrating coming together – especially suited to morning assemblies. For added fun, a simple second part is built into the chorus. There is also a short 5-bar middle section (as featured in the introduction), which may require a more careful listen.	5+	PSHE; Positive attitude	Upbeat with a swing
Good Morning	This simple song is equally at home in assemblies as it is in the classroom at register time. The recording features examples of both a general and a more personalised version. With a simple echo and space for specific names to be included, this song gives scope for individual children/groups to take a lead, and for the class to respond.	5+	PSHE; Encouragement	Cheerfully
It's Nearly Playtime	Written in a style that has become a familiar feature of Out of the Ark Music publications, this catchy song will have your class singing and toe-tapping as they tidy up ready for playtime, lunch-time or home-time!	5+	PSHE; Organization	Upbeat with a swing
I Have A Song To Sing	As songs go, they don't come much shorter or simpler than this but, my goodness, you can make such an impression with it. It's a song of unity and coming together, building momentum along the way. Sincere, uplifting and great for morning assemblies.	5+	Music; PSHE; Unity	Ethereal & building
Just Sing!	We expect this will become a firm favourite in schools across the land. A defining 'statement song', which unashamedly waves the banner for singing in schools everywhere. Beware, you may find yourself singing some very unlikely lyrics, but you'll have great fun doing it!	5+	Music; Singing	Latin flavour
Sing A Round	This one simply does what it says in the title! The lyrics in this fun song are all about the process and musical elements of round-singing. Each new part is sung twice, to give scope for solo/group work, before the song is sung as a round. (An alternative piano arrangement in G major is also available on the website at www.outoftheark.com - search for 'Songs for EVERY Singing School'.)	7+	Music; Singing	Morris music style

All the songs in this book are teachable by anyone and everyone. If you have no prior knowledge of music education, we recommend you start with a graded music activity which will help you begin to open up the musical possibilities within the songs. You'll soon realize there's nothing to be scared of! The following key, shown on each activity page, will help give an indication of how confident you can be in delivering the given activity:

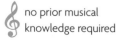 no prior musical knowledge required   some basic knowledge of rhythm or notation may be helpful   a reasonable grasp of music fundamentals would be an advantage

Vocal range	Key	Musical elements	Music activity	Inter-related dimensions
Medium (C#-C)	G	• Syncopation • Melodic leaps	Get 'in sync with syncopation' by learning about how to compose and perform syncopated rhythms. Either using group clapping or playing instruments to perform to each other in smaller groups.	
Large (B-C#)	E	• Syncopation • Call & response	Use chimes or other tuned percussion instruments to improvise simple 'call and response' melodies to develop skills of listening to others' musical ideas.	
Medium (C-C)	C	• Solo or group singing • Syncopation • Call & response	Younger children will enjoy this pitch practice activity by using a 'call and response' melody with their own names. Great for recognizing high and low pitch.	
Medium (B-C)	G	• Syncopation • Melodic leaps	Introduce musical vocabulary of how sound is produced in either legato or staccato style by 'scarfing around' – using scarves to demonstrate the differences by moving in time to the music of *It's Nearly Playtime*.	
Medium (B-C#)	E-F#	• Solo or group singing • Modulation • Syncopation • Melodic leaps	Using simple rhythmic mnemonics, this activity will enable children to recognize texture in music by performing layers of rhythms in groups either by clapping or playing percussion instruments.	
Large (F-D)	B♭	• Syncopation • Articulation • Melodic leaps	Have fun composing some new lyrics for *Just Sing!* using recurring syllabic rhythm/rhyme patterns. Your lips and tongue will be buzzing with all the fabulously 'chewable' words you could choose.	
Medium (C#-C#)	F#	• Round singing • Syncopation • Melodic leaps • $\frac{6}{8}$ time signature	Try some suggested morris dancing steps to perform for each of the different parts of *Sing A Round*.	

Icon Key

 Dynamics   Pitch Rhythm/duration   Structure Timbre   Texture   Tempo   Notation Articulation

7

SONG INFORMATION

Song	Song summary	Age	Subject	Musical style
Sing Anyway	A good choice of song for exercising diction and dynamics, while having a great time in the process. The more work that's put into vocal expression, the greater the satisfaction will be. Not one of you will be able to sing half-heartedly!	5+	Music; Singing	Cheerful
New Day Blues	Written for sleepyheads everywhere, this entertaining song will generate good levels of energy and wake everyone up in the morning! Even the most reluctant of singers should enjoy this one. The modulation and change of tempo at the end will require some direction.	7+	PSHE; Organization	Blues
Sun Arise	A simple melody with bags of atmosphere and plenty of optimism. The inclusion of simple crescendos and an optional small harmony line allow for good expression. A great way to start any school day.	5+	PSHE; Joy; Praise	Triumphant
Take A Major Scale	Use this song to help your children write their own songs! While describing the song-writing process, it provides a simple structure of syllables/numbers of lines/rhyme pattern, with some helpful lyric-writing tips. The children can use this template for trying out some ideas of their own. Much potential for enormous creativity is built into this wacky little number!	7+	Music; Composing	Upbeat
Take 5 Styles	A bit of a first from 'Out of the Ark', this song demonstrates how one basic melody can be adapted to five very different musical styles, (samba, swing, waltz, tango and Israeli) with minimal lyric changes. It's actually a good deal easier than it sounds, and lends itself very well to some varied and energetic dancing. Hugely rewarding with just a little work.	7+	Music; Musical genres	Samba, Swing, Waltz, Tango, Israeli (Klezmer)
School Is Nearly Over	The second round in this collection, but there's no reason why this can't be sung 'straight' with younger children. A simple song ideal for use at the end of any school day, with or without accompaniment.	5+	PSHE; Daily routine; Music	Steady
Thank You Lord	A very easy-to-learn song of gratitude, sung with a simple echo throughout the verses (great for dividing in two – girls/boys, older/younger etc). A really rousing chorus will make this a firm favourite in assemblies, services etc.	5+	PSHE; Appreciation	Joyful
We Are One	The anthem of this songbook. It highlights the value of singing together and the sense of strength and belonging that come from it. This song features a strong two-part harmony in the chorus, which is worth any effort it takes to master.	5+	PSHE; Belonging	Anthemic

All the songs in this book are teachable by anyone and everyone. If you have no prior knowledge of music education, we recommend you start with a 🎼 graded music activity which will help you begin to open up the musical possibilities within the songs. You'll soon realize there's nothing to be scared of! The following key, shown on each activity page, will help give an indication of how confident you can be in delivering the given activity:

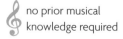 no prior musical knowledge required

some basic knowledge of rhythm or notation may be helpful

a reasonable grasp of music fundamentals would be an advantage

Vocal range	Key	Musical elements	Music activity	Inter-related dimensions
Large (C-D)	F	• Syncopation • Articulation • Melodic leaps	Continuing the dynamic variations of *Sing Anyway*, this activity will get children to assume different body actions for different dynamics. Includes using the first movement of Beethoven's *Fifth Symphony* as a suggested listening exercise.	
Medium (B-C)	E-F	• Modulation • Syncopation • Tempo changes	Investigate the style, characteristics and 12-bar structure of the Blues by accompanying *New Day Blues* on tuned percussion instruments.	
Medium (C-C)	C-D	• Harmony singing • Modulation • Syncopation	Compose a 'soundscape' replicating the sounds of a morning sunrise by learning about the different timbres of percussion instruments as well as playing together as an ensemble.	
Medium (B-C)	B-C	• Syncopation • Melodic leaps	Listen to and evaluate the structure and rhythms of *Take A Major Scale* in order to create new lyrics to the song. Use the resource sheet provided to get the creative juices flowing to produce some inspired new lyrics.	
Large (D-E♭)	Gm	• Syncopation • Tempo & time signature changes	Use percussion instruments to accompany *Take 5 Styles* and experience what is required to change one's instrumental playing style in a variety of musical genres by using different accents, time signatures and tempos.	
Medium (C-C)	C	• Round singing • Syncopation • Melodic leaps	Add some fun marching and arm actions to the song, performing these in sequence as the round is sung..	
Medium (C♯-C♯)	A	• Syncopation • Call & Response	Develop listening and instrumental playing skills by playing the call-and-response rhythms from *Thank You Lord* on drums or other percussion instruments.	
Large (B-C)	G	• Part singing • Syncopation	Investigate the use of countermelodies in music, as used in the two-part section of *We Are One*, by listening to and evaluating the music of *One Day More* from *Les Miserables*.	

Dynamics Pitch Rhythm/duration Structure Timbre Texture Tempo Notation Articulation

IF YOU CAN WALK, YOU CAN DANCE

Based on the Zimbabwe Proverb, 'If you can walk, you can dance; if you can talk, you can sing.'

CHORUS

If you can walk, you can dance,
If you can talk, you can sing.
If you can move, you can grow,
If you can breathe, you can live!

1   Just one step at a time,
    You won't know till you try.
    You will find it's OK,
    Make the most of today!

CHORUS

2   Throw your worries aside,
    Lose your 'reason and rhyme'.
    There's no getting it wrong,
    If you're moving along!

CHORUS

3   Just one step at a time,
    You won't know till you try.
    You will find it's OK,
    Make the most of today!
    (Repeat)

Words and Music by Mark and Helen Johnson
© 2007 & 2015 Out of the Ark Ltd, Middlesex TW12 2HD
CCLI Song No. 5079746

TEACHING TIPS:

- Encourage the children to listen to each other so that they come off together on the last word of each phrase. It will help if you warm voices (and bodies) up well before singing to give the song the energy and positivity it deserves.

- Be aware of the leaps in the melody. Take big breaths before each line of the chorus so that you can really punch out the notes on key words such as *'walk'*, *'talk'*, *'move'* and *'grow'*.

Notation   Improvise

Sing   Listen

Play   Compose

Genre/History/Musicians

WHAT YOU NEED

Large space; good clapping hands; tuned/untuned percussion instruments

ACTIVITY

AGES 7 - 11

Get the children to stand in a circle and steadily chant the following together:

'1 and 2 and 3 and 4 and 5 and 6 and 7 and 8 and'

Repeat this a few times and then add claps to the numbers only (giving you a **regular beat**).

Next, divide the circle in half and get one half to **clap on the beat (the numbers)** and the other to **clap off the beat (the 'ands')**. Swap the groups over so everyone has a turn clapping on and off the beat. Which do they find easiest to do? Now, rather than counting aloud, get the children to **start to internalize the beat in their heads**, still clapping on the beats and offbeats.

Discuss the definition of **syncopation** and refer to the rhythms of the chorus of *If You Can Walk, You Can Dance*. Get the children to walk in time to the beat while one half claps along with their steps (on the beat) and the others clap the **syncopated rhythm** of the chorus. They should begin to recognize how the rhythm falls differently to the steps of their feet! Swap groups.

STEP IT UP!

Have some fun making your own syncopated rhythms using the counting from the main activity. Split into four groups and get group one to clap a slow, steady beat. Then, ask the other groups to **choose a number from 1-8**. Each group will then **clap only the 'and'** after the number their group has chosen, such as:

*'1 **and** 2 and 3 and 4 and 5 **and** 6 **and** 7 and 8 and'*
(if they chose 1, 5 and 6)

Adapt the activity by **increasing the tempo** as appropriate and choosing different numbered 'and's to change the rhythm. **Try introducing instruments** in place of claps to create a class performance.

WHAT'S ACHIEVABLE?

To identify a syncopated rhythm through counting and clapping.

To perform a syncopated rhythm accurately and in time as an ensemble.

RHYTHM

Syncopation – placement of notes off the main beat

TEMPO

The speed of the music

WE'RE HERE AGAIN

1   We're here together and the day is new.
There's a song in our hearts and a shine on our shoes.
We're here together and we welcome you.
It's a day we can share and there's plenty to do.

> CHORUS

*We're here again
With all our friends,
We're here today
To learn and play.*

2   We're here together and the day is new.
There's a smile on my face and a positive view.
We're here together and we welcome you.
It's a day we can give and a day we can choose.

> CHORUS

Just a simple song,
Needn't take too long,
It will help you on your way!

3   *Repeat verse 1*

> CHORUS

*We're here again (all together)
With all our friends, (everyone sing!)
We're here today (good to see 'ya')
To learn and play.*

Just a simple song,
Needn't take too long,
It will help you on your way!

> CHORUS X 2

Words and Music by Mark and Helen Johnson
© 2007 & 2015 Out of the Ark Ltd, Middlesex TW12 2HD
CCLI Song No. 5079722

TEACHING TIPS:

- **Listen to the song** a few times with the children before you begin singing. You'll find that so much of the teaching is done for you this way, as the catchy melody is so memorable. Try some warm-up vocal exercises too, making sure the voice is ready to begin work on the song. This will especially help the production of the first note (B) on 'We're', which is quite low in the children's vocal range.

- The children will love the **call & response parts** towards the end of the song. If you listen carefully to the backing track while singing the second chorus, you'll notice the melody of the response is there – subliminally working away in the choir's minds, ready for later in the song. Experiment with different divisions of voices (older/younger, girls/boys etc.)

- Take a little time to look at the short middle section. The melody for this is featured in the introduction and may require a more careful listen to perfect.

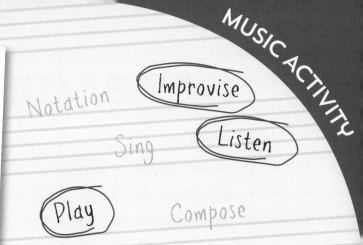

Notation   Improvise
Sing   Listen
Play   Compose
Genre/History/Musicians

WHAT YOU NEED 🔧

Chimes or other tuned percussion instruments in the key of C

ACTIVITY  AGES 7 - 11

Try the following activity with **non-verbal instructions**. Distribute tuned percussion instruments to all the children (keeping one for yourself) and get them to play 'C, D, E, rest' together over four beats and in time on their instrument. Establishing a clear beat by keeping your melodic instruction regular and in time, will help the children to play in time together.

Next, instruct everyone to play 'C, D, E, rest' together by giving the same visual signal each time, such as thumbs up. After they play together, you **'respond' with a different melody and rhythm** using the same three notes. Continue this repeatedly and then ask the children to discuss what you were doing.
(You were providing a 'response' to their 'call'.)

Then, play the 'C, D, E, rest' melody and point to individual children to 'respond'. Melodic responses should be in the same time, with a slightly different melody and rhythm to the 'call'. Play the 'C, D, E, rest' melody after each individual has **improvised**. Sticking to the notes in the C major scale (C, D, E, F, G, A, B), increase the number of notes used depending on the age and ability of the group.

SPOTLIGHT ON 🔦
CALL & RESPONSE

When musicians respond to each other in music, it corresponds to the question-and-answer pattern in vocal communication. Sometimes answers are echoed and sometimes they include part of the 'question' in the 'answer' with a slight variation.

LISTEN

Experience a master at work by listening to **Mozart's** use of **call and response** in his Papageno Papagena Duet from *The Magic Flute.*

STRUCTURE 🧊

Call and Response – a musical phrase in which the first melody or rhythm is responded to or echoed by another melody or rhythm

WHAT'S 🎖
ACHIEVABLE?

To perform on an instrument in time as an ensemble.

To play a complementary, improvised melodic response to a question.

PITCH 〰

How high or low a note sits

Scale – an arrangement of notes in ascending or descending order of pitch

GOOD MORNING

Version 1 – Group greeting

Good morning! *(Good morning!)*
It's really good to see you.
Good morning! *(Good morning!)*
We're glad that you are here.
When we do the register
It's good to hear each name.
If ever there's anyone missing,
It's never the same!

Version 2 – Individual greeting

Good morning! *(Good morning!)*
It's good to see you _____.
Good morning! *(Good morning!)*
We're glad that you are here.
When we do the register
It's good to hear each name.
If ever there's anyone missing,
It's never the same!
If ever there's anyone missing,
It's never the same!

Words and Music by Mark and Helen Johnson
© 2007 & 2015 Out of the Ark Ltd, Middlesex TW12 2HD
CCLI Song No. 5079708

TEACHING TIPS:

- This is a simple, repetitive song that the children should find easy to learn. There is a danger of them either speeding ahead or dragging behind the tempo – neither of which you want – so encourage them to listen carefully to the strong beat given by the backing track and to sing along in time.

- If you're using this song without the backing track, try playing a loud percussion instrument in time with the choir to keep everyone together or ask the children to walk on the spot to the beat.

- Hopefully each child will be confident enough to sing individually either as a 'caller' or 'responder', otherwise ask the class to join in all together as you work through all the names of the group.

Notation   Improvise

(Sing)   (Listen)

Play   Compose

Genre/History/Musicians

WHAT YOU NEED

Pre-agreed hand gestures
(e.g. Sol-fa hand gestures)

ACTIVITY   AGES 4 - 7

Try some **pitch-perfect practice!**

Ask the children to **count how many syllables** their name contains. Using the example of 'An-dy' from *Good Morning*, this has two syllables, which **rise in pitch (D-G)**. Use your hand to indicate the rise in pitch, either choosing your own actions for each note or **sol-fa actions**:

 Re    Sol

Discuss the direction of pitch with the children and how notes can be **higher or lower**.

Next, ask each child to individually **sing their name** using the hand signals and the same two notes as in the song. Explain that those with longer names (e.g. Al-ex-an-der) will need to decide on which syllable to rise in pitch. Will it be on the 'ex', 'an' or 'der' syllables? Let the children decide, although some may need support.

LISTEN 🔊

Discover how Oscar Hammerstein II uses pitch in *The Lonely Goatherd* from *The Sound of Music*. As the melody jumps around, try standing tall for the high notes and crouching down for the low.

SPOTLIGHT ON PITCH

The frequency of soundwave vibrations determines how high or low a pitch is, therefore the length of strings or the air tunnel of an instrument affects whether these vibrations are short/high (piccolo) or long/low (tuba). The pitch of the voice depends on the length and thickness of the vocal cords, which is why men often have lower voices than women. Our voices can also be affected by emotions, going higher when we're excited or frightened as our muscles contract! Experiment with the pitch of your voice – how high or low can you safely go?

WHAT'S ACHIEVABLE?

To recognize changes in pitch.

To recall and sing at the correct pitch.

PITCH 〰

How high or low a note sits

Sol-fa (short for Tonic Sol-fa) – a set of syllables (do, re, mi, fa, so, la, ti) used to represent the tones of the musical scale, each of which has a corresponding hand symbol

IT'S NEARLY PLAYTIME*

1 It's nearly playtime,
It's clear-away time,
It's time to tidy up.
It's nearly playtime,
We need to take a break,
We've all worked hard enough!
(Repeat)

Every day there's lots to do,
Everybody needs a break or two.
Exercise, rest your eyes, take some time,
Do as you choose.

2 INSTRUMENTAL

Every day there's lots to do,
Everybody needs a break or two.
Exercise, rest your eyes, take some time,
Do as you choose.

3 *Repeat verse 1*

We've all worked hard enough!

IT'S NEARLY LUNCHTIME
It's nearly lunchtime,
It's 'feed your tum' time,
It's time to get some food.
It's nearly lunchtime,
I'm looking forward to mine,
I hope it's something good!

IT'S NEARLY HOME TIME
It's nearly home time,
It's 'cheerio' time,
It's time to say goodbye.
It's nearly home time,
We'll grab our bags and coats
And leave our work behind!

* Take your pick from the lyrics above according to the occasion!

Words and Music by Mark and Helen Johnson
© 2007 & 2015 Out of the Ark Ltd, Middlesex TW12 2HD
CCLI Song No. 5079760

TEACHING TIPS:

- The verses of this song will work really well with actions. Think of some appropriate actions and try teaching the repeated part of the verse by getting children to:

  1) follow the actions in time without lyrics

  2) teach the lyrics with actions but without singing

  3) after teaching the melody, sing with actions

  This a great way to develop children's watching and listening skills.

- Throughout the instrumental section you can assess internal recognition of rhythm by getting the children to repeat the actions in time, just like when learning the verse.

- Focus on the correct pitch for the longer held notes of 'play' and '(a)way', as well as the F♮ notes 'every**day**' and 'every**bo**dy', by practising a few times through.

Notation   Improvise

Sing   Listen

Play   Compose

Genre/History/Musicians

ACTIVITY

AGES 6 - 9

Have some fun 'scarfing around' with this activity!

Help the children to recognize the different **musical articulation** in *It's Nearly Playtime* by demonstrating the actions below for each section of the song:

Section A (**verse** – *'It's nearly playtime…'*):
hold the scarf top and bottom, pull it down on each beat of the bar in a 'spiky' (staccato) manner while walking to the beat.

Section B (**bridge** – *'Everyday there's lots to do…'*):
move the scarf side-to-side in a smooth (legato) manner, changing direction every second beat.

Section C (**instrumental**):
move the scarf in a big circle, from the top all the way around and back to the top over each 4-beat duration (bar).

Ask the children to describe your scarf actions for the different sections of the song. Are they smooth, jerky, spiky, soft, fast, slow etc.? Start to **introduce vocabulary of staccato and legato**.

Distribute scarves to each of the children to repeat the same actions throughout the song while listening to the backing track and walking in time with the music.

WHAT YOU NEED

Lightweight scarves or pieces of material for each child; large space; amplified sound system

LISTEN

Listen to different movements from Camille Saint-Saëns' *Carnival of the Animals*, such as *The Aquarium, Kangaroos, March of the Lions* or *The Swan*, which all include both legato and staccato articulation in the music. Perhaps the children can replicate the scarf activity while listening.

STRUCTURE

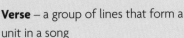

Verse – a group of lines that form a unit in a song

Instrumental – a part of a song that is played without lyrics (often using the familiar chord structure of the verse or chorus)

Bridge – a passage of music that connects one section of a song to another (often referred to as the middle 8)

ARTICULATION

Legato – smoothly

Staccato – detached

WHAT'S ACHIEVABLE?

To recognize and define different articulation in music.

To recognize organization of structure in music.

To perform movement rhythmically and in time to music.

I HAVE A SONG TO SING

The important thing with this song is to build up the vocal sound each time it's sung through – from single voice to mass vocal sound.

I have a song to bring,
It has a simple melody.
Let everybody sing,
There's life in our unity,
There's hope in our song.

Last time:
I have a song to bring,
It has a simple melody.
Let everybody sing,
There's life in our unity,
There's hope in our song.
There's life in our unity,
There's hope in our song.

Words and Music by Mark and Helen Johnson
© 2007 & 2015 Out of the Ark Ltd, Middlesex TW12 2HD
CCLI Song No. 5079674

TEACHING TIPS:

- Experiment with musical texture by trying different combinations of voices (younger/older; girls/boys; solo/groups etc.). In a classroom context try using the song as a game, allowing the first child to select the next singer(s) to join in. Enjoy the way this song builds and go for the biggest sound you can to finish (perhaps all the adults could join in last time through!)

- Discuss the concept of 'dense' and 'sparse' texture in music. Listening to the instrumental backing track, try listing all the instruments that join in and build texture throughout the song.

- The song builds musical intensity as it modulates throughout, but do practise the key-change sections a few times to hear and sing these correctly.

Notation   Improvise

Sing   Listen

Play   Compose

Genre/History/Musicians

WHAT YOU NEED

Large space; untuned percussion instruments

ACTIVITY   AGES 7 - 11

Investigate how texture is created
in music by building up layered rhythms.

Divide the class into three groups and assign each group one of the following rhythmic patterns (all of which should be familiar as they are taken from the first line of the song):

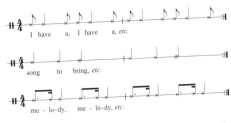

Get each group to start by saying their rhythm separately, then combine the groups one layer at a time, like **building a rhythm wall.** Once you have mastered this, ask the children to clap the rhythms instead of speaking. Finally, assign percussion instruments to each group and start to play the layered rhythms together as a class ensemble.

LOOK! 👀

Go to **www.outoftheark.com** to view the wonderful **signing video** that we've produced for this song. Sing along and sign the words to add another dimension to your performance!

STEP IT UP! 🚀

Try adding your **percussion ostinatos** to the song, playing as you sing. Starting with just one rhythmic motif, introduce layers as the verse repeats to build up the texture as the song progresses.

WHAT'S 🏅 ACHIEVABLE?

To recognize and recall rhythms using a rhythmic mnemonic.

To perform rhythms as an ensemble, accurately and in time.

To recognize the difference between sparse and dense texture.

RHYTHM 🥁

Ostinato – repeated rhythmic or melodic pattern

Polyrhythm – the simultaneous use of two or more different rhythms

TEXTURE △

Layers of sound and rhythm

JUST SING!

1 Sing when you're happy, sing when you're sad,
   Sing when you're laughing, sing though it's mad,
   Sing 'Howdy-doody', sing 'Toodle-oo', just sing!

2 Sing when it's sunny, sing when it's grey,
   Sing when it's raining, sing every day,
   Sing 'Hallelujah', sing 'Wackadoo', just sing!

   CHORUS   *Don't you worry if it's heard or not,*
             Keep on singing, give it all you've got,
             Just sing!

3 Sing when it's easy, sing when it's not,
   Sing in pyjamas, sing in your socks,
   Sing 'Humpty Dumpty', sing 'Kangaroo', just sing!

   CHORUS

4 Sing in the garden, sing in the bath,
   Sing for your supper, sing for a laugh,
   Sing 'Mashed potato', sing 'Vindaloo', just sing!

5 Sing with a whisper, sing very loud,
   Sing when you're lonely, sing in a crowd,
   Sing grandioso! Sing out the blues, just sing!

   CHORUS

             Don't you worry if it's heard or not,
             Keep on singing, give it all you've got,
             Don't you worry if it's heard or not,
             Keep on singing, give it all you've got,
             Just sing!... Just sing!... Just sing!... etc.

Words and Music by Mark and Helen Johnson
© 2007 & 2015 Out of the Ark Ltd, Middlesex TW12 2HD
CCLI Song No. 5079643

TEACHING TIPS:

- This song will work very well with two groups, each singing alternate phrases and everyone singing the chorus and the phrase *'just sing!'*

- Make sure you attack the **syncopated rhythms** with energy. Try standing to sing the song and get the children to change position every time they sing the word *'sing'*.

- In the chorus, before attempting to sing, get the children to clap the rhythm and say the words out loud in time. Then introduce the melody.

Notation   Improvise

Sing   Listen

Play   Compose

Genre/History/Musicians

WHAT YOU NEED 🔧
White/black board;
Just Sing! backing track

ACTIVITY
AGES 6 - 11 🎼

Draw attention to the language in the last line of each verse (e.g. *Humpty Dumpty/kangaroo; mashed potato/ vindaloo*). Observe the **recurring rhythm/rhyme pattern.** There are four syllables in the first phrase (*Hump-ty-Dump-ty*) and three in the second (*kan-ga-roo*). Also, the second word or phrase always ends with an *'oo'* rhyme.

Write some new 'last lines' and try them out:

'Sing... (4 syllables), sing... (3 syllables/oo rhyme), just sing!'

Think about using **words that are fun to sing** – ones that make your tongue and lips move a lot or ones that make you smile. Which of your new lyrics are the most enjoyable to sing? Why?

Sing the song through with all your new lyrics!

BRIGHT IDEA! 💡
Very often we teach songs without talking about the content. Take some time to discuss the children's **experience of singing**. **When** do they sing? **Where** do they sing? **Why?** What about other people in their **family**? Do they have any concept of the **benefits** of singing?

DID YOU KNOW? ❓
Singing is good for you! What other single activity do you know of that has the capacity to:
- improve lung-capacity and circulation;
- improve posture, confidence and self-esteem;
- enhance mental alertness and creativity;
- reduce blood pressure and anxiety;
- boost the immune system;
- release pain-relieving endorphins and muscle tension;
- exercise all the major muscle groups in the upper body;
- improve your mood at the same time (by releasing the same 'feel-good' endorphins as chocolate)?

All with no cost or calories!
This singing stuff is good!

WHAT'S 🎗 ACHIEVABLE?
To recognize recurring rhythm and rhyme patterns in lyrics.

To compose lyrics within a given rhythmic and rhyming scheme.

RHYTHM 🥁
Duration/length of notes; regular, repeated patterns of sound

Syncopation – placement of notes off the main beat

SING A ROUND

1   We'll sing a round,
        You'll hear a number of melodies,
        It's quite a sound
        When we are singing all three.
        (Repeat)

2   Put the rhythm in your feet,
        Keep a very steady beat.
        Try to make each word you speak
        Clear as clear can be.
        (Repeat)

3   Sing your melody to make a harmony,
        Sing your melody and make it sweet.
        (Repeat)

Repeat all verses as a round (without repeats)

Words and Music by Mark and Helen Johnson
© 2007 & 2015 Out of the Ark Ltd, Middlesex TW12 2HD
CCLI Song No. 5079753

TEACHING TIPS:

- Singing **rounds** is a fantastic way of getting younger children to start singing in harmony. It's important for the whole choir to learn all parts of the round first before separating into three different parts.

- When the children are singing each of the three parts of the round, try assigning a different body-percussion action to each different melody part (e.g. pat, clap, snap or stomp).

Notation   Improvise

Sing   Listen

Play   Compose

Genre/History/Musicians

WHAT YOU NEED 🔧

Large space for dancing; handkerchiefs (optional); amplified sound system

ACTIVITY

AGES 7 - 11 🎼

Using the three-part groups for *Sing A Round*, **create some morris dance choreography**, giving each part a different dance step to perform while singing together.

Start **'We'll sing a round'** with the **single morris step**:

Beat 1   step forward with the left foot
Beat 2   hop on the left foot *(while lifting and extending the right leg forward without bending the knee)*
Beat 3   step on the right foot
Beat 4   hop on the right foot *(while lifting and·extending the left leg forward without bending the knee)*

Repeat stepping backwards rather than forwards, and so on.

For **'Put the rhythm in your feet'** use the **double morris step**:

Beat 1   step forward with the left foot
Beat 2   step forward with the right foot
Beat 3   step forward with the left foot *(while lifting and extending the right leg forward without bending the knee)*
Beat 4   hop on the left foot

Repeat starting on the right foot but stepping backwards rather than forwards, and so on.

'Sing your melody' can be a more fluid, side-to-side step while raising both arms first to the left, then to the right. **Add some handkerchiefs** for an authentic morris dance style! This will get exciting when all three parts are sung together as a round.

BRIGHT IDEA! 💡

Try a **rhythmic round** to practise performing different rhythms as part of a group: sit in a circle and ask each child to copy the person next to them. Demonstrate a rhythm *(e.g. four knee pats)* to the first child who should then repeat this and pass it on to the next person and so on. The rhythm will then work its way around the circle. As this is happening, introduce a new pattern *(e.g. four clicks)* to the first child to then pass on. Add as many rhythms as you want, until the first rhythm gets back to the first child again, at which point you can continue all the rhythms for as long as you like!

WHAT'S ACHIEVABLE? 🎖️

To recall and maintain a melodic part while singing with others.

To maintain a steady beat with movement.

STRUCTURE

Round (canon) – a song for three or more parts, each starting one after another with the same melody, creating a polyphonic effect as they overlap.

RHYTHM 🥁

Ostinato – repeated rhythmic or melodic pattern

TEXTURE ⚠️

Layers of sound and rhythm

Polyphony – the simultaneous combination of a number of parts, each forming an individual melody and harmonizing with each other

SING ANYWAY

CHORUS *There's a happy sound of singing today,*
With a little 'Tra-la-la-la'
And a little 'Ooo-la! Olay!'
There's a happy feeling coming my way,
With a bit of 'Oom-pa, oom-pa'
And a lot of 'Tru-ra-lie-ay',
With a touch of 'Shooby-doo-wah'
And a load of 'Yippee-aye-ay!'

1   Sing whatever comes to mind,
Maybe you can find a rhyme.
Keep it smiley, keep in time, but sing anyway!

CHORUS

2   See what lines you can invent,
Even if it makes no sense.
You can just experiment and sing anyway!

CHORUS

3   Sing whatever comes to mind,
Maybe you can find a rhyme.
Keep it smiley, keep in time, but sing anyway!
*(Sing twice – first time **f**, second time **pp**)*

CHORUS

4   See what lines you can invent,
Even if it makes no sense.
You can just experiment and sing anyway!
*(Sing twice – first time **f**, second time **pp**, with **crescendo** last line)*

Words and Music by Mark and Helen Johnson
© 2007 & 2015 Out of the Ark Ltd, Middlesex TW12 2HD
CCLI Song No. 5079681

TEACHING TIPS:

- A good tongue-twister warm-up will be effective before you start to sing this song, as there are some fabulously aerobic-style lyrics for the mouth here. Try our *S!ng Warm-ups* collection for inspiration.

- Try not to let the offbeat vocal entry at the beginning catch you out. It may be helpful to use this **rest** as an opportunity for a quick breath, and again before the words *'today'* and *'my way'*.

- This song uses a **range of dynamics** that are specified on the lyrics page. Explain that singing quietly is not using a 'whisper' voice, nor is singing loudly using a 'shouty' voice, but rather that air, supported by the diaphragm, should be used to produce a clear, tuneful voice with more or less volume.

Notation   Improvise

Sing   Listen

Play   Compose

Genre/History/Musicians

WHAT YOU NEED

White/black board; large space; amplified sound system; Beethoven's *Fifth Symphony* (optional)

ACTIVITY

AGES 4 - 9

Create a list of **body actions** that correspond to different **music dynamics** to help children to understand and demonstrate various levels of volume in music.

Practise by using music that you can either adapt in volume or that demonstrates different dynamics throughout the piece – the first movement of **Beethoven's *Fifth Symphony*** is a great example to work with.

The following dynamic vocabulary and actions could be used:

Pianissimo (**pp**): both index fingers on lips

Piano (**p**): one finger on lips

Mezzo piano (**mp**) or mezzo forte (**mf**): hands behind ears

Forte (**f**): fists clenched

Fortissimo (**ff**): arms out to the side and fingers stretched

Try to add **decrescendos** and **crescendos** to your body actions! Finally, ask the children to sing *Sing Anyway* using the same body actions to replicate the dynamics in the song.

BRIGHT IDEA!

To familiarize the children with dynamics vocabulary, **try a 'hot vs. cold' humming warm-up game**. One child (the 'seeker') turns their back while another hides an object in the room. The rest of the group will then hum quietly (piano) when the seeker is far away from the hidden object or loudly (forte) when the seeker is closer, using decrescendos and crescendos accordingly as the seeker searches the room. Try experimenting with different pitches and syllables for each new 'seeker' volunteer.

DYNAMICS

Volume

Pianissimo *pp* – very soft/quiet

Piano *p* – soft/quiet

Mezzo piano *mp* – moderately soft

Mezzo forte *mf* – moderately loud

Forte *f* – loud

Fortissimo *ff* – very loud

Crescendo – a gradual increase in volume and intensity

Decrescendo – a gradual decrease in volume and intensity

RHYTHM

Rest – a period of silence of a specified duration

WHAT'S ACHIEVABLE?

To recognize differences in dynamic levels in music.

To define different dynamic levels using musical vocabulary.

Sing Anyway

NEW DAY BLUES

1   When I woke up this morning,
    I heard my **mama** calling:
    'You'd better get up, get out, get on your way!'
    I stayed in my bed,
    I buried my head
    From the new day.

2   When I woke up this morning,
    I heard my **papa** calling:
    'You'd better get up, get out, get on your way!'
    I stayed in my bed,
    I buried my head
    From the new day.

3   When I woke up this morning,
    I heard my **sister** calling:
    'You'd better get up, get out, get on your way!'
    I stayed in my bed,
    I buried my head
    From the new day.

4   When I woke up this morning,
    I heard my **brother** calling:
    'You'd better get up, get out, get on your way!'
    I stayed in my bed,
    I buried my head
    From the new day.

5   When I woke up this morning,
    I heard my **family** calling:
    'You'd better get up, get out, get on your way!'
    I got out of bed,
    And here's what I said:
    I said 'OK!'

Words and Music by Mark and Helen Johnson
© 2007 & 2015 Out of the Ark Ltd, Middlesex TW12 2HD
CCLI Song No. 5079667

TEACHING TIPS:

- Try teaching this song in a call-and-response manner. The short four-bar phrases are easy for the children to recall and repeat after you.

- Watch out for the **'blues' note** on the word *get **out*** as this may require a little more practice in order for all the children to pitch the note correctly. Explain that a 'blues' note is common in this style of song.

- The children will love to sing the paused *'O-K!'* at the end of the song and the more expression and dramatics the better! Just ensure that they watch you in order to keep together.

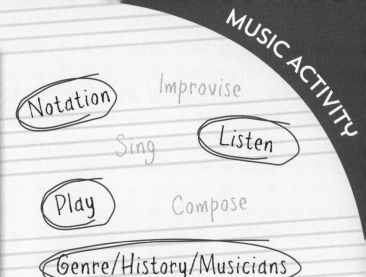

Notation Improvise Sing Listen Play Compose

Genre/History/Musicians

WHAT YOU NEED
Amplified sound system; white/black board; tuned percussion instruments; Internet access

ACTIVITY
AGES 7 - 11

LISTEN
Listen to three different versions of the **Blues song** *Hound Dog,* by Elvis Presley, Eric Clapton and Willie Mae 'Big Mama' Thornton (the original version). Evaluate how the song evolved at different times and through different artists. What are the musical differences between the versions heard (e.g. instrumentation, use of instrumental solos, swing style, lyrics)?

Try accompanying *New Day Blues* with a **'Blues riff'** on melodic instruments. Write the following notes on the board and play them as a **repeated ostinato** throughout using the rhythm sung on *'morning'* and *'new day'*.

E E | E E | E E | E E |

A A | A A | E E | E E |

B B | A A | E E | E E |

After a period of practice, try playing along with the backing track. (At the key change, move the pattern up a semitone to F.)

F F | F F F | F F F | F F |

B♭ B♭ | B♭ B♭ B♭ | F F | F F |

C C | B♭ B♭ B♭ | F F | F F |

SPOTLIGHT ON
BLUES MUSIC

The Blues is a style of music that **originated in the southern states of the USA** where communities sang spirituals, work songs and chants as an **expression of their oppression** due to racism and segregation. The genre developed a distinctive **structure of twelve bars and a cyclical chord pattern** that combined African melodies and rhythms with a more Western European musical structure. Melodies are often improvised or composed on the spot over a repeated chord structure.

WHAT'S ACHIEVABLE?
To evaluate the 12-bar structure of a Blues form.

To play a Blues riff in a 12-bar Blues structure.

To recognize and define the musical characteristics of Blues music.

PITCH
How high or low a note sits

Blues note – a note which is flattened by a semitone (or less), usually found on the 3rd, 5th or 7th degree of the scale

STRUCTURE
12-bar Blues – a distinctive chord progression based around the I-IV-V chords of a key

RHYTHM
Ostinato – repeated rhythmic or melodic pattern

New Day Blues

SUN ARISE

1   Sun arise – see a new day dawn,
    Spread your light on a sleeping world,
    Arise! Let the morning come.
    Sun arise – let the day begin,
    Fill the skies, put the colours in,
    Arise! Let the morning come.
    Arise! Let the morning come.

CHORUS   *Shake off your slumber,*
         Awake to the wonder of sun-rising.
         Take up the chorus of life,
         There's a glorious song to sing!

2   There's a call – to a brand-new day,
    Greet the dawn with a song of praise,
    Arise! Let the morning come.
    There's a call – let the song go round,
    Fill the earth with a joyful sound,
    Arise! Let the morning come.
    Arise! Let the morning come.

CHORUS

3   Sun arise – see a new day dawn,
    Spread your light on a sleeping world,
    Arise! Let the morning come.
    Sun arise – let the day begin,
    Fill the skies, put the colours in,
    Arise! Let the morning come.
    Arise! Let the morning come.
    Arise! Let the morning come.
    Arise! Let the morning come.

Words and Music by Mark and Helen Johnson
© 2007 & 2015 Out of the Ark Ltd, Middlesex TW12 2HD
CCLI Song No. 5079715

TEACHING TIPS:

- When rehearsing this song, take some time to concentrate on the long note(s) on the word *'arise'*. Make sure the singers take a good breath before this word and hold it, building with intensity, right to the end. The children should be watching you as you 'close' the end of the word to ensure the 's's sound together. You can decide how to signal this – one way is to swoop the arm round in a circular motion, closing the fingers of your hand together right at the end of the sung note.

- Another technique to help the children sing to the end of the note is to get them to raise their arms in a rainbow arch while singing the word so that aurally and visually they are reaching right to the end of the phrase.

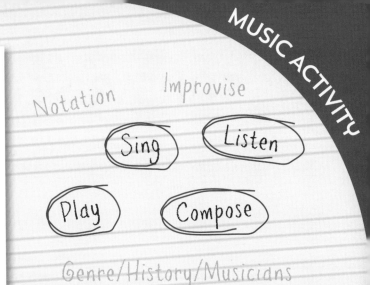

Notation   Improvise

Sing   Listen

Play   Compose

Genre/History/Musicians

WHAT YOU NEED
Tuned & untuned percussion instruments; amplified sound system

ACTIVITY
AGES 6 - 11

Create a morning-nature soundscape using different instruments to represent different sounds, such as whistles or whistling for **birds singing**, shakers for **rustling trees**, chimes for the **blowing breeze**, sliding down a glockenspiel for **falling leaves**, triangles for **rain on the windows** or any number of creative sounds that you can devise with the children.

Discuss the concept of different **instrumental timbres** and the effect created by these different sounds. When your collection of sounds is complete, try starting with a few soft sound effects as if the morning is just beginning and then gradually add more to create **a cacophony of morning-nature noise!** Think of a story to help the children remember the order.

Try performing the soundscape as an introduction that leads into a performance of *Sun Arise*.

LISTEN
How have other composers interpreted the theme of morning? Listen to *Morning* from *Peer Gynt Suite No. 1* by Edvard Grieg and get the children to **draw what they hear**. This will make a great display for the 'music board'.

BRIGHT IDEA!
Divide the children into groups, giving different percussion instruments to each group (wooden, metallic, drums, tuned etc.) and get them to **create an ostinato** on their instruments to play throughout the song.

For the long held notes of *'arise'* in the 2nd verse, get children to play the notes on tuned percussion instruments (G and the B-C harmony notes).

WHAT'S ACHIEVABLE?
To recognize different instrumental timbres and their effects.

To compose an effective soundscape story with instruments.

To perform a soundscape as an ensemble.

TIMBRE
The character or quality of a musical sound

Tone colour of instruments: low/high; soft/hard; metallic/wooden/stringed/wind

RHYTHM
Ostinato – repeated rhythmic or melodic pattern

TAKE A MAJOR SCALE

1   Do–re–mi–fa–so–la–ti–do, so,
Take a major scale and choose some words you know.
Make a simple song,
Needn't be too long.
Do–re–mi–fa–so–la–ti–do, la–so–do.

2   Anything you want to say is fine,
Doesn't even have to have a perfect rhyme.
Do the best you can,
Make the lyrics scan.
Only choose the words that seem to fit in time.

3   'Humpty Dumpty sat upon a wall',
You can play around with any words at all.
Make it fun to sing,
Try out anything.
'Humpty Dumpty had a rather nasty fall!'

4   Writing songs can be a lot of fun,
Singing them is really good for everyone.
You will never know
Till you have a go.
You may be surprised at just how well you've done!
You may be surprised at just how well you've done!

Words and Music by Mark and Helen Johnson
© 2007 & 2015 Out of the Ark Ltd, Middlesex TW12 2HD
CCLI Song No. 5079739

TEACHING TIPS:

- With all the **focus on scales** in this song, it almost feels like a vocal warm-up in itself, but it's a good idea to loosen up the vocal cords before you start and there are lots of vocal range extension warm-ups to try in our *S!ng Warm-ups* collection if you need some ideas.

- If the children are familiar with the **Tonic Sol-fa** sight-singing method, they will recognize the **Do-re-mi lyrics** in this song. This is a great opportunity to practise the hand signals that accompany each note of the scale *(these can easily be found online)*. Why not also test the children's aural recognition skills by asking them to sing the note that relates to each hand signal without singing it for them?

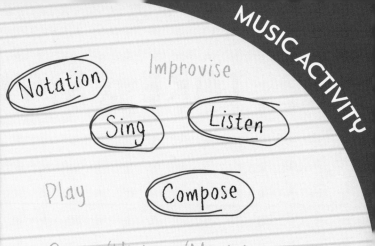

Notation Improvise Sing Listen Play Compose

Genre/History/Musicians

WHAT YOU NEED

Amplified sound system; *Write Your Own Song* worksheets (p94); pencils.

ACTIVITY

AGES 6 - 11

Take A Major Scale is designed so that children can **write their own lyrics** by using a **simple worksheet** that allows new words to be added to the melody of the song, dependent on the number of syllables in each line.

First, **establish the structure of the song**: ask the children to stand while listening to the backing track. They should sit, or bob down, when they hear the shape of the melody change (as in *'make a simple song'*) and stand again when it changes back (*'Do-re-mi-fa-so-la-ti-do'*). Give each section (standing or sitting) a letter name, A or B. It should be clear now that the structure of the melody is A-A-B-B-A. Ask the children which section is shorter, A or B.

Next, provide the group with the *Write Your Own Song* worksheet (p94), which outlines how many syllables are allocated to each line and the rhyming pattern for each verse. Why not **set a theme for songwriting**, such as a topic you're studying in the classroom or an occasion that's coming up in the calendar? Ask for volunteers to sing their new song and the children could then **perform their favourite new songs** together with the backing track.

SPOTLIGHT ON SONGWRITING

Try these **suggestions to give inspiration and new ideas** for songwriting:

- Keep a **notebook or diary** with you at all times – you never know when inspiration will strike!

- Get inspired by **great works of fiction or art** like many other artists have (Nat King Cole's *Mona Lisa*, Dire Straits' *Romeo and Juliet* and Kate Bush's *Wuthering Heights*).

- Look for inspiration everywhere, for example the titles of **magazine articles**, which are often snappy and can make great starting points for songs.

- **Immerse yourself in listening** to great music.

PITCH

How high or low a note sits

Scale – an arrangement of notes in ascending or descending order of pitch

Sol-fa (short for Tonic Sol-fa) – a set of syllables (do, re, mi, fa, so, la, ti) used to represent the tones of the musical scale, each of which has a corresponding hand symbol

STRUCTURE

The organization of a piece of music into sections, e.g. ABA

WHAT'S ACHIEVABLE?

To recognize rhythmic syllabic placement in music using lyrics.

To recognize and define structure in music.

To compose lyrics that fit with a given melody.

Take A Major Scale

TAKE 5 STYLES

Samba

CHORUS *There are many ways you can sing a tune,*
Take a style to suit your mood.
(Repeat)

Music's playing,
What's it saying
To the rhythm in your feet?
If you feel the
Song you're singing,
It's amazing, you'll agree!

Swing Jazz

CHORUS *There are many ways you can sing a tune,*
Take a style to suit your mood.
(Repeat)

When the music's playing,
Hear what it is saying,
Can you feel the rhythm in your feet?
Feel what you are hearing
In the song you're singing,
It's a lovely feeling, you'll agree!

Classical Waltz

CHORUS *There are many ways to sing a tune,*
You'll need to choose your mood.
(Repeat)

Music's playing,
What's it saying
To the rhythm in your feet?
If you feel the
Song you're singing,
It's amazing, you'll agree!

Tango

CHORUS *There are many ways to sing a tune,*
A style will suit your mood.
(Repeat)

When the music is playing,
Try and hear what it's saying.
You can follow the rhythm in your feet.
If you feel what you're hearing,
In the song that you're singing,
It's a wonderful feeling, you'll agree!

Israeli

CHORUS *There are many ways that you*
can sing a tune,
Just choose yourself a style
to suit your mood.
(Repeat)

When the music's playing,
Hear what it is saying,
Can you feel the rhythm in your feet?
Feel what you are hearing
In the song you're singing,
It's a lovely feeling, you'll agree!

There are many ways to sing a tune.
Doodle-oo-doo, doodle-oo!
Yeah!

Words and Music by Mark and Helen Johnson
© 2007 & 2015 Out of the Ark Ltd, Middlesex TW12 2HD
CCLI Song No. 5079698

TEACHING TIPS:

- Once you have listened to this song a few times, you will really start to feel the difference between these styles! The instrumental introductions between the changes of style are very important to set up the feel for the next section of the song, particularly where there is a change of time signature.

- Focus on learning the different rhythmic accents for each style, as this will help the children to internalize the change of beat and rhythms. Highlight how the *Samba, Tango* and *Israeli* styles are sung with short, **staccato** notes while the *Swing* and *Waltz* styles are more relaxed and **legato**.

- Ask the children to speak the words in time before singing the melody to help learn the rhythm. To **feel the differences between styles**, try clapping different core rhythms such as a syncopated swing rhythm, a tango rhythm or the regular offbeat of the Israeli style.

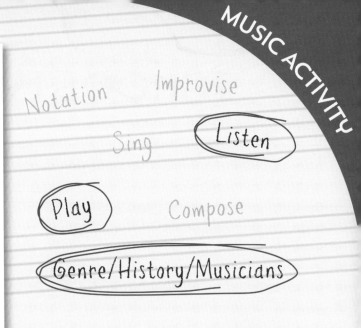

Notation   Improvise   Sing   Listen   Play   Compose   Genre/History/Musicians

ACTIVITY
AGES 9 - 11

Accompany the different musical styles of *Take 5 Styles* **on percussion instruments.**

Seat the children in a circle and assign every other person a **woodblock or claves.** The remaining children should be given **shaker instruments.** Each group of instruments will play on a different beat of the bar: **shakers on strong beats (1 & 3)** and **claves on the offbeats (2 & 4)**. Practise first before playing along with the backing track. To help, provide a count-in during the introduction of each of the five different styles.

During each musical style, the children will need to adapt the **tempo** and **articulation** of their playing. For the waltz, the **time signature** changes to $\frac{6}{8}$ so counting will change to '**1**, 2, 3, **4**, 5, 6'. In this time signature get the shakers to play on beats 1 & 4 and the claves on 2, 3 & 5, 6 (*'shake, tap, tap, shake, tap, tap'*). Be careful not to play too fast for the Israeli style as the drums play 'double time' here!

Ensure that each style is played in time, stopping and reviewing if required. For added difficulty *(fun!)*, try asking the children to swap instruments after each style, handing their shaker or woodblock to the person next to them to play on the appropriate beats!

WHAT YOU NEED
Shakers and wooden sticks/claves; amplified sound system, *Take 5 Styles* backing track.

LISTEN
Classical composers use a technique known as '**Variations**' to vary and change a piece of music. Listen to **Haydn's Symphony No. 94 'Surprise'** **– 2nd movement**, beginning with the main theme. Discuss the variations throughout the piece such as dynamics, countermelodies, minor key, different instruments repeating the main theme etc. Use **Charles Ives'** **Variations on America** to repeat the same activity.

RHYTHM
Pulse – the beat, or steady heartbeat of the music

Time signature – an indication of rhythm/metre that gives the number of beats per bar

ARTICULATION
The style of the execution of a musical note, e.g. spiky or smooth

Legato – smoothly

Staccato – detached

TEMPO
The speed of the music

WHAT'S ACHIEVABLE?
To recognize changes to musical **pulse**.

To perform accurately in different tempos and time signatures.

To demonstrate appropriate **articulation** on instruments in different styles of music.

SCHOOL IS NEARLY OVER

This is a very simple round – it could easily be managed unaccompanied in the classroom at the end of the day, with as many parts as there are table groups.

School is nearly over and it's time to go.
We've got lots of things to do when we get home.
Cheerio! See you soon.
Don't forget to come back in the morning!*

* 'in the morning' can be changed to 'Monday morning' if sung on a Friday!

Words and Music by Mark and Helen Johnson
© 2007 & 2015 Out of the Ark Ltd, Middlesex TW12 2HD
CCLI Song No. 5079791

TEACHING TIPS:

- This **round** is great for adding rising and falling hand movements with the melody as the children sing. Once they have learnt the song, ask them to show you how **the melody rises and falls in pitch** with their hands by moving them as they sing the song.

- To sing the round, split the class into four groups from left to right. Start the left group singing and then indicate for the next group along to sing from the beginning as the first group start their 2nd phrase (*'We've got lots of things to do when we get home.'*) Introduce the third and fourth groups in the same way (after each phrase (two bars)).

- Children should continue using hand movements to follow the melody while singing in different groups, as this is a great learning activity for pitch and useful for you to visually assess accuracy when they are in different groups.

Notation   Improvise

Sing   Listen

Play   Compose

Genre/History/Musicians

ACTIVITY   AGES 5 - 9

WHAT YOU NEED
Large space; 'marchy' children!

Once you're familiar with the song and singing it together in a round, **add some fun marching actions**.

Staying in your four groups, line up one behind the other in a big snake ready to march around the room. Group one should decide on a sequence of four arm actions, one to go with each phrase while they are marching. **Make the actions big** so the other groups will be able to see.

As the music starts, everyone begins to march on the beat and snake around the room. As group one begin to sing, they should perform the first arm action. When they reach the 2nd phrase, group two begin to sing, copying the first arm action as group one begin the second phrase and the second arm action. Keep going until all groups are singing, imitating the arm actions in sequence as they go. Continue the round in this way until group four has reached the end of the song.

DID YOU KNOW?
Rounds have been around since medieval times when they were called **'rota'** or **'rondellus'**. The oldest surviving English round is *Summer Is Icumen In* which is for 4 voices with an additional 2 bass voices singing a never-changing repeating part (a ground). **Three Blind Mice** is one of the earliest published rounds and **Shakespeare** mentions various well-known rounds in his plays, proving that they were popular during Elizabethan times too.

WHAT'S ACHIEVABLE?
To recall and maintain a melodic part while singing with others.
To maintain a steady beat with movement.

STRUCTURE
Round (canon) – a song for three or more parts, each starting one after another with the same melody, creating a polyphonic effect as they overlap.

TEXTURE
Layers of sound and rhythm

Polyphony – the simultaneous combination of a number of parts, each forming an individual melody and harmonizing with each other

RHYTHM
Beat – the pulse, or steady heartbeat of the music

THANK YOU LORD

1   Thank you Lord, (thank you Lord)
    For this day, (for this day)
    For your love, (for your love)
    In all we do!
    Thank you now, (thank you now)
    For our school, (for our school)
    For our friends, (for our friends)
    All we can do.

CHORUS   *We want to say thank you for this day,*
         We want to say thank you Lord always.
         We want to say thank you God, in everything,
         'Cause all you give is good!

2   Thank you Lord, (thank you Lord)
    For our homes, (for our homes)
    For our food, (for our food)
    All that you give!
    Thank you now, (thank you now)
    We can laugh, (we can laugh)
    We can sing, (we can sing)
    Learn as we live.

CHORUS

3   Thank you Lord, (thank you Lord)
    For this world, (for this world)
    All you've made, (all you've made)
    All that you do!
    Thank you now, (thank you now)
    For my life, (for my life)
    For your care, (for your care)
    All that is You!

CHORUS X 2

         'Cause all you give is good!
         'Cause all you give is good!

Words and Music by Mark and Helen Johnson
© 2007 & 2015 Out of the Ark Ltd, Middlesex TW12 2HD
CCLI Song No. 5079777

TEACHING TIPS:

- A physical warm-up will put some energy into this song – try the following:

  Get the children to space out and step side-to-side counting 1-2-3-4. When that is established, call **1-2-3-Ho**, where on 'Ho' they fling their arms high. Then change to **1-2-Ha**, where on 'Ha' they fling their arms forward. Now divide the group into two. Get one to do the *1-2-3-Ho* and one to do the *1-2-Ha*, all at the same time.

- Start off teaching this song by singing the first phrase and getting the children to respond. Then, try choosing one child to do the 'call' part with everyone else responding. You could spread the 'call' lines amongst several children. Alternatively, you could use larger groups such as KS1 and KS2 for the call and response.

- Raise the **dynamics** in the chorus by getting everyone to sing together.

Notation   Improvise

 Sing    Listen

Play   Compose

Genre/History/Musicians

WHAT YOU NEED
Amplified sound system; drums or percussion instruments

ACTIVITY

AGES 6 - 11

Investigate the technique of 'call and response' in music with the following activities.

Direct the children to **start a steady four-beat rhythm using body percussion**, e.g. clapping and patting: clap, pat, clap, pat. In time, ask different individuals the question, *'What's for din-ner?'*. Each child should respond vocally with an answer that is rhythmically in time and within the steady four-beat pattern, for example *'fish and chips'*.

Next, **distribute percussion instruments to the group** – ideally drums, but other percussion instruments will work just as well. Repeat the 'question and answer' activity above using instruments so that individual children can play their responses. Only those responding should be playing instruments; the rest should maintain the steady four-beat body-percussion pulse.

Finally, divide the group in two with one group **singing the 'call'** during each verse of *Thank You Lord*, and the second group **playing the rhythmic response** on their instruments with the backing track. All should join together to sing *'in all we do!'* and the chorus. Swap groups that sing or play for each verse.

BRIGHT IDEA!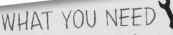

Invite the children to **compose their own rhythmic ostinato** to accompany the chorus and perform together as a class along with the backing track.

LISTEN

There are countless numbers of artists who have given thanks through song. Have a listen to some and discuss the similarities and differences. Here are a few to get you started:

Thank You (Dido)
Thank You For The Music (Abba)
(Thank You For The) Days (Kinks)

WHAT'S ACHIEVABLE?

To respond to rhythmic 'questions' with appropriate 'answers' in time.
To perform rhythms accurately in time.
To compose an ostinato to perform as a rhythmic accompaniment as an ensemble.

STRUCTURE

Call and Response – a musical phrase in which the first melody or rhythm is responded to or echoed by another melody or rhythm

RHYTHM

Pulse – the beat, or steady heartbeat of the music

Ostinato – repeated rhythmic or melodic pattern

Thank You Lord

WE ARE ONE

1   There are people in our lives,
Some are friends and some are strangers.
Though we see through different eyes,
And we come from many places.

CHORUS A

We are one, we are strong,
As we sing our songs together.
We are one, we belong,
As we share our lives together.

2   There are places in our lives,
There are things we've done together.
And the memory of these times
Will be in our hearts forever.

CHORUS B

Together we are strong,
We sing our songs together.
Each one of us belongs,
We share our lives together.

3   There are seasons in our lives,
And they bring us many changes.
Through the low times and the highs,
As we turn our separate pages.

CHORUS [A] and [B] together TWICE

LAST CHORUS

We are one, we are strong,
As we sing our songs together.
We are one, we belong,
As we share our lives together.

Words and Music by Mark and Helen Johnson
© 2007 & 2015 Out of the Ark Ltd, Middlesex TW12 2HD
CCLI Song No. 5079784

TEACHING TIPS:

- The melody has a large vocal range and some big leaps, so **warming up your voice before singing** is important. Take a rubber band and, as you sing a scale, stretch it as the voice goes up and relax it as it comes back down again. This visual aid will help the children to see where their voices are going and give them an idea of where they are within their vocal range.

- You'll find the **two-part singing easy to teach** as both parts are featured separately earlier in the song. Make sure the children know these parts well before attempting to put them together.

- If you are lucky enough to have any **recorder players**, they could join in with each of the parts in the two-part section. The notes sit comfortably on the instrument and it will really help the singers to keep to the correct pitch.

Notation Improvise Sing Listen

Play Compose

Genre/History/Musicians

WHAT YOU NEED 🔧

White/black board; amplified sound system; Internet

ACTIVITY AGES 7 - 11

Look at **countermelodies** in more detail.

Place the four bars of the two-part section from *We Are One* on the board – see below

This shows the notation of the **melody** and **countermelody** without lyrics.

Divide the group into the parts they usually sing for the song, then get them to try to **follow the notation** on the board as they sing along. Ask the children to decide with a partner which line of notation pattern matches the part that they were singing and to be ready to feed back their reasons to the class.

Encourage partners to clap rhythms and look at the direction (up or down) of the notes, to help with their decision.

LISTEN 🔊

Listen to *One Day More!* from *Les Miserables* and ask the children to see if they can count how many different melodies are used throughout. It's a sophisticated example of **countermelodic writing** involving recalling themes from previous songs and characters and combining together into one song.

SPOTLIGHT ON
TEXTURE

In music, a **countermelody** is a secondary melody played simultaneously with a more prominent lead melody, as demonstrated in the two-part section of *We Are One*. It adds interest to music and produces a **dense texture** or **layers of music** played together in a complementary way. **Polyphonic** (poly meaning many, phonic meaning voice) music includes **multiple melodic 'voices'** either independent from or relating to each other.

WHAT'S 🎖 ACHIEVABLE?

To recognize rhythmic patterns in notation related to aural sounds.

To define texture in music.

To recognize countermelodies in musical examples.

PITCH 〰

Countermelody – a subordinate melody accompanying a principal one

TEXTURE ⛰

Layers of sound and rhythm

We Are One

IF YOU CAN WALK, YOU CAN DANCE

Words and Music by
Mark and Helen Johnson

1. 3. 𝄉 Just one step at a time,___ you won't know till you try.___
2. Throw your wor-ries a-side,___ lose your 'rea-son and rhyme'.___

To Coda ⊕

You will find it's O-K,___ make the most of to-day!___
There's no get-ting it wrong, if you're mov-ing a-long!___

1. 2.

If you can

3. *D. 𝄉 al Coda* ⊕ **CODA**

make the most of to-day!

41

WE'RE HERE AGAIN

Words and Music by
Mark and Helen Johnson

GOOD MORNING

Words and Music by
Mark and Helen Johnson

Cheerfully ♩ = 94

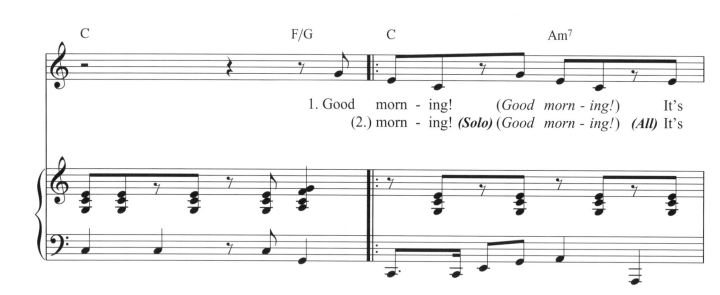

1. Good morn - ing! *(Good morn - ing!)* It's
(2.) morn - ing! *(Solo) (Good morn - ing!) (All)* It's

real - ly good to see you. Good morn - ing! *(Good morn - ing!)* We're
good to see you *An - dy.** Good morn - ing! *(Solo) (Good morn - ing!) (All)* We're

* Substitute any name.

IT'S NEARLY PLAYTIME*

Words and Music by
Mark and Helen Johnson

1. It's near-ly play - time,— it's clear-a-
(2. Instrumental)

- way time,— it's time— to ti - dy up. It's near - ly

* Playtime can be replaced by *lunchtime* or *home time* as suitable. See alternative lyrics on p16.

play - time,_ we need to take a break, we've all___ worked hard_ e-nough!

1. It's near-ly

2. Ev - ery day there's lots to do,

ev - ery - bo - dy needs a break_ or two.   Ex - er - cise, rest your eyes,

take some time, do as you choose.

To Coda ⊕   N.C.

D.S al Coda

2. *Instrumental*

I HAVE A SONG TO SING

Words and Music by
Mark and Helen Johnson

Always building ♩ = 98

1° Solo, 2° Trio, 3° All

1. 2. 3. I have a song to bring, it has a sim-ple me-lo-dy.

Let ev-ery-bo-dy sing, there's life in our u-ni-ty, there's

hope in our song. song.

4. 5. I have a song to bring, it has a sim - ple

me - lo - dy. Let ev - ery - bo - dy sing, there's

life in our u - ni - ty, there's hope in our

1. song. **2.** song. 6. I have a song to

JUST SING!

Words and Music by
Mark and Helen Johnson

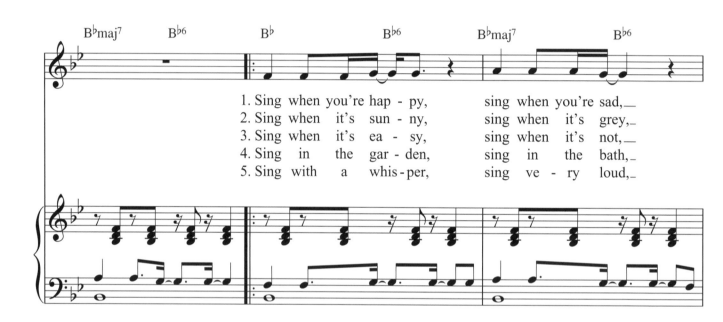

1. Sing when you're hap - py,   sing when you're sad,__
2. Sing when it's sun - ny,   sing when it's grey,__
3. Sing when it's ea - sy,   sing when it's not,__
4. Sing in the gar - den,   sing in the bath,_
5. Sing with a whis - per,   sing ve - ry loud,__

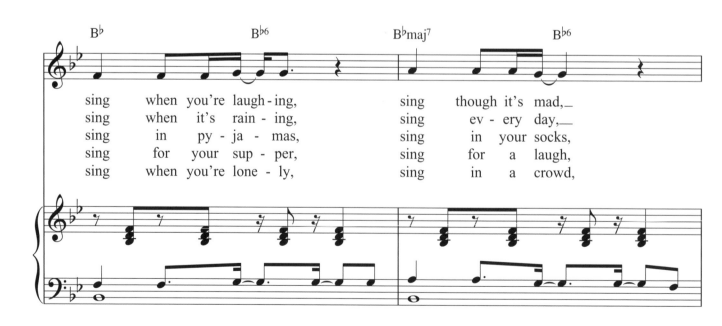

sing when you're laugh - ing,   sing though it's mad,__
sing when it's rain - ing,   sing ev - ery day,__
sing in py - ja - mas,   sing in your socks,
sing for your sup - per,   sing for a laugh,
sing when you're lone - ly,   sing in a crowd,

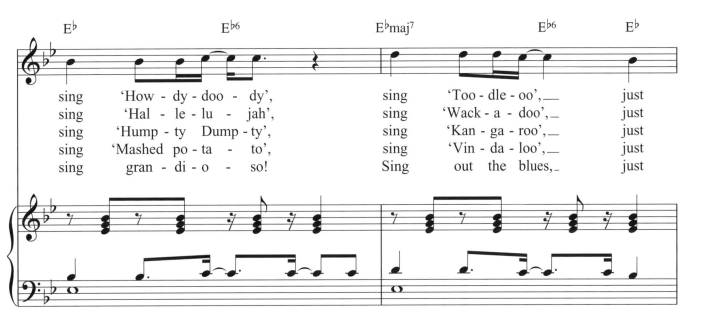

sing 'How - dy - doo - dy', sing 'Too - dle - oo', __ just
sing 'Hal - le - lu - jah', sing 'Wack - a - doo', __ just
sing 'Hump - ty Dump - ty', sing 'Kan - ga - roo', __ just
sing 'Mashed po - ta - to', sing 'Vin - da - loo', __ just
sing gran - di - o - so! Sing out the blues, __ just

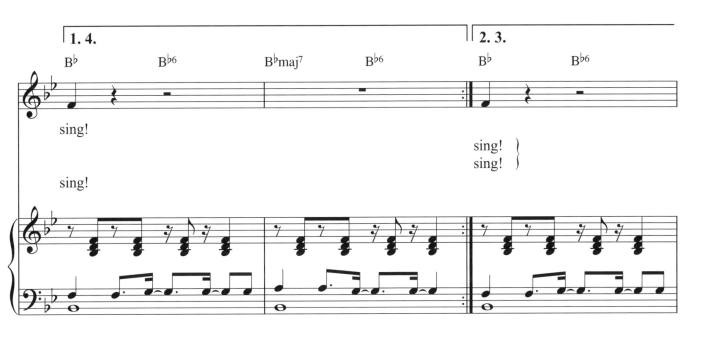

1. 4.

sing!

sing!

2. 3.

sing!
sing!

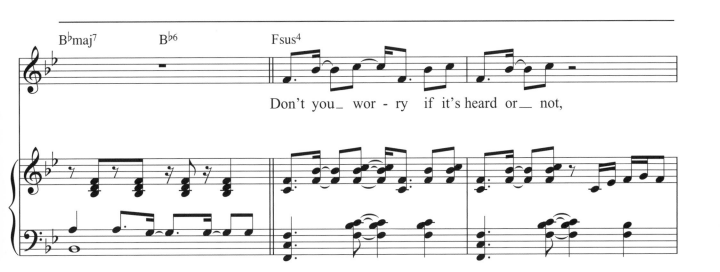

Don't you_ wor - ry if it's heard or __ not,

keep on__ sing-ing, give it all you've got, just sing!

sing!

Don't you__ wor - ry if it's

heard or__ not, keep on__ sing - ing, give it all you've got,

SING A ROUND

Words and Music by
Mark and Helen Johnson

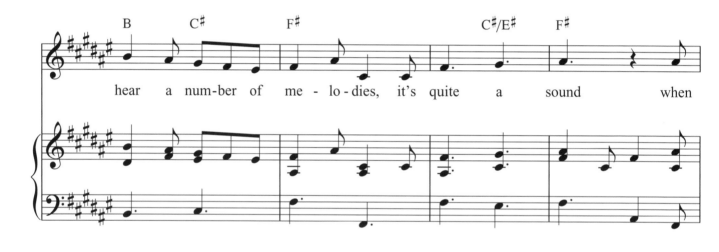

If preferred, an alternative version of this piece arranged in G major is available for download from our website, www.outoftheark.com

61

SING ANYWAY

Words and Music by
Mark and Helen Johnson

Cheerfully ♩ = 116
Gm7 C Am D7 Gm7 C
F B♭/C F B♭/C F C7sus4 F Gm F/A
There's a hap-py sound of
B♭ F/A B♭ F/A C C/E
sing - ing to - day, with a lit - tle 'Tra - la - la - la' and a lit - tle
F Gm7 F/A C7sus4 F Gm F/A B♭ F/A B♭ F/A
'Ooo - la! O - lay!' There's a hap-py feel-ing com-ing my way, with a bit of

'Oom - pa, oom - pa' and a lot of 'Tru - ra - lie - ay', with a touch of

'Shoo - by - doo - wah' and a load of 'Yip - pee - aye - ay!'

1. Sing what - ev - er comes to mind, may - be you can find a rhyme.
2. See what lines you can in - vent, e - ven if it makes no sense.

Keep it smi - ley, keep in time, but sing a - ny - way!
You can just ex - pe - ri - ment and sing a - ny - way!

64

'Tra - la - la - la' and a lit - tle 'Ooo - la! O - lay!' There's a hap - py feel - ing

com - ing my way, with a bit of 'Oom - pa, oom - pa' and a lot of

'Tru - ra - lie - ay', with a touch of 'Shoo - by - doo - wah' and a load of

'Yip - pee - aye - ay!' You can just ex - pe - ri - ment and sing a - ny - way!

NEW DAY BLUES

Words and Music by
Mark and Helen Johnson

1. When I woke up this morn - ing,— I heard my **ma - ma**
(2.) I woke up this morn - ing,— I heard my **pa - pa**
(3.) I woke up this morn - ing,— I heard my **sis - ter**
(4.) I woke up this morn - ing,— I heard my **bro - ther**

call - ing:— 'You'd bet-ter get up, get out, get on your way!'—

5. When I woke up this morn - ing, __ I
heard my **fam - ily** call - ing: __ 'You'd bet - ter get up, get
out, get on your way!' __ I got out of bed, and
here's what I said: I said 'O - K!' _____

SUN ARISE

Words and Music by
Mark and Helen Johnson

With strength ♩ = 110

1. Sun a - rise,___ see a new day___ dawn,___ spread your___ light___ on a
2. There's a___ call___ to a brand - new___ day,___ greet the___ dawn___ with a

sleep - ing___ world, a - rise!_____ Let the
song of___ praise, a - rise!_____ Let the

Shake off___ your slum - ber,___ a - wake to___ the won - der___ of

sun - ris - ing.___

Take up___ the cho - rus___ of

life, there's a glo - ri - ous song to___ sing!___

3. Sun a - rise,___ see a new day___ dawn,

TAKE A MAJOR SCALE

Words and Music by
Mark and Helen Johnson

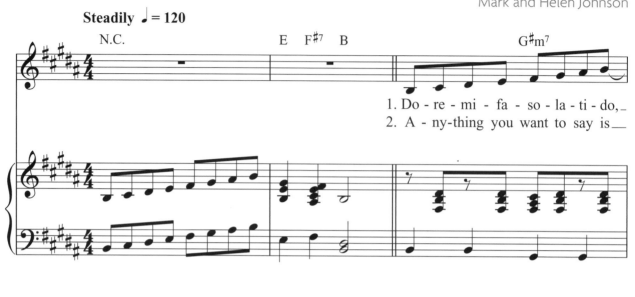

TAKE 5 STYLES

Words and Music by
Mark and Helen Johnson

There are ma - ny ways you can sing a tune, take a style to
suit your mood. When the mu-sic's play - ing, hear___ what it is say - ing,
can you feel the rhy - thm in your feet? Feel what you are hear - ing in___
___ the song you're sing - ing, it's a love-ly feel - ing, you'll a - gree!

SCHOOL IS NEARLY OVER

Words and Music by
Mark and Helen Johnson

1-4. School is near-ly o-ver and it's time to go. We've got lots of things to do when we get home. Chee - ri - o! See you soon.

Don't for-get to come back in the morn - ing!* morn - ing!*

* 'in the morning' can be changed to 'Monday morning' if sung on a Friday!

THANK YOU LORD

Words and Music by
Mark and Helen Johnson

1. Thank you Lord, (thank you Lord) for this day,— (for this day)
2. Thank you Lord, (thank you Lord) for our homes, (for our homes)
3. Thank you Lord, (thank you Lord) for this world, (for this world)

for your love, (for your love) in all__ we do!
for our food, (for our food) all that__ you give!
all you've made, (all you've made) all that__ you do!

WE ARE ONE

Words and Music by
Mark and Helen Johnson

GLOSSARY

3/4 a time signature indicating three crotchet beats per bar

4/4 a time signature indicating four crotchet beats per bar

12-bar Blues a distinctive chord progression based around the I-IV-V chords of a key

3-2 Clave a three-beat, two-beat Latin rhythm

Adagio at a slow, leisurely pace

Allegro at a brisk speed

Andante at a walking pace

Arpeggio the notes of a chord played in succession, either ascending or descending

Articulation the style of the execution of a musical note, e.g. spiky or smooth

Bar a short section or measure of music, with a specific number of beats

Beat the pulse, or steady heartbeat of the music

Bar line a vertical line used in musical notation to mark the division between bars

Blues note a note which is flattened by a semitone (or less), usually found on the 3rd, 5th or 7th degree of the scale

Bridge a passage of music that connects one section of a song to another (often referred to as the middle 8)

Call & Response a musical phrase in which the first melody or rhythm is responded to or echoed by another melody or rhythm

Chord a group of (typically three or more) notes sounded together, as a basis of harmony

Chorus a part of a song that is repeated after each verse

Chromatic where notes ascend or descend by semitones

Clef a musical symbol placed at the left-hand end of a stave, indicating the pitch of the notes written on it

Compound time signature where strong beats are subdivided by three rather than two

Consonant harmony that attains to the key or mode of the music; a combination of notes that create a conventionally pleasing sound

Countermelody a subordinate melody accompanying a principal one

Crescendo a gradual increase in volume

Cross-rhythm a rhythm used simultaneously with another rhythm

Crotchet a musical note with a time value equal to two quavers

Cumulative song a song with a simple verse structure whereby the original lyrics stay the same on each repetition and an additional line or lyric is added for each new verse

Decrescendo a gradual decrease in volume

Diminuendo a gradual decrease in volume

Dissonant not attaining to any key or mode; a combination of notes that clash with one another and create a lack of pleasing harmony

Drone a continuous musical note, often of low pitch

Dynamics volume

Forte loud

Fortissimo very loud

Harmony the combination of simultaneously sounded musical notes

Instrumental a part of a song that is played without lyrics (often using the familiar chord structure of the verse or chorus)

Interval the difference in pitch between two sounds

Key a group of notes that correspond to a certain scale and form the tonal centre of a section of music

Largo slowly and broadly

Legato smoothly

Lento slowly

Major key based on a major scale and tending to produce a bright, joyful effect

Major scale a series of notes mostly separated by intervals of a tone, but having intervals of a semitone between the 3rd and 4th and 7th and 8th degrees

Melody the arrangement of single notes that create a satisfying musical sequence

Mezzo forte moderately loud

Mezzo piano moderately soft/quiet

Minim a musical note with a time value equal to two crotchets

Minor key based on a minor scale and tending to produce a sad or pensive effect

Minor scale	a series of notes mostly separated by intervals of a tone, but having intervals of a semitone between the 2nd and 3rd degrees and (usually) the 5th and 6th and the 7th and 8th
Moderato	moderately
Modulation	the change from one key (tonal centre) to another
Musical form	the overall structure or plan of a piece of music
Notation	a system of written symbols used to visually represent aurally perceived music
Octave	the difference in sound (interval) between the 1st and 8th notes in a musical scale. These notes share the same letter name, with the top note (e.g. C) having twice the frequency of vibration of the bottom note (C)
Offbeat	any of the normally unaccented beats in a bar
Ostinato	repeated rhythmic or melodic pattern
Pentatonic scale	a five-note scale pattern
Phrase	a group of notes forming a distinct unit within a longer passage
Pianissimo	very soft/quiet
Piano	soft/quiet
Pitch	how high or low a note sits
Polyphony	the simultaneous combination of a number of parts, each forming an individual melody and harmonizing with each other
Polyrhythm	the simultaneous use of two or more different rhythms
Presto	quickly
Pulse	the beat, or steady heartbeat of the music
Quaver	a musical note with a time value equal to half a crotchet
Rest	a period of silence of a specified duration
Rhythm	duration/length of notes; regular, repeated patterns of sound
Ritardando	a gradual decrease in speed
Rondo	a musical form with a recurring leading theme that alternates with one or more contrasting themes, such as ABA, ABACA or ABACABA
Root note	the fundamental note of a chord
Round	(canon) – a song for three or more parts, each starting one after another with the same melody, creating a polyphonic effect as they overlap.
Scale	an arrangement of notes in ascending or descending order of pitch
Semibreve	a musical note with a time value equal to two minims or four crotchets
Semiquaver	a musical note with a time value equal to half a quaver
Semitone	the interval between two adjacent notes on a piano or the smallest interval commonly used in classical Western music
Sequence	a repetition of a phrase or melody at a higher or lower pitch
Shuffle	a rhythmic motif based on a shuffle dance step and typical of early jazz, consisting of alternating crotchets and quavers played with a triplet feel
Sol-fa (short for Tonic Sol-fa)	a set of syllables (do, re, mi, fa, sol, la, ti) used to represent the tones of the musical scale, each of which has a corresponding hand symbol
Staccato	detached
Stave	a set of five parallel lines on which notes are written to indicate pitch
Structure	the organization of a piece of music into sections, i.e. ABA
Swung quavers	a musical technique of playing two quavers where the first is held for slightly longer than the second, giving an underlying triplet feel
Syncopation	placement of notes off the main beat
Tempo	the speed of the music
Texture	layers of rhythm and sound
Timbre	the character or quality of a musical sound; tone colour of instruments: low/high; soft/hard; metallic/wooden/stringed/wind
Time signature	an indication of rhythm/metre that gives the number of beats per bar
Tonality	the harmonic effect of being in a particular key
Tremolo	a wavering effect in a musical tone produced by a rapid repetition of a single tone, or alternating tones
Verse	a group of lines that form a unit in a song
Vivace	in a lively and brisk manner

WRITE YOUR OWN SONG

Name: _____

Using the 1st verse from *Take A Major Scale*, as a template, try writing your own lyrics to the tune of this song. Each space equals one syllable, and lines (A) should rhyme with each other, as should lines (B).

Do – re – mi – fa – so – la – ti – do , so , (A)

Take a ma – jor scale and choose some words you know. (A)

Make a sim–ple song, (B)

Need–n't be too long. (B)

Do – re – mi – fa – so – la – ti – do , la – so – do . (A)

Title of song: _____

1   _____ (A)

     _____ (A)

     _____ (B)

     _____ (B)

     _____ (A)

2   _____ (A)

     _____ (A)

     _____ (B)

     _____ (B)

     _____ (A)

COPYRIGHT & LICENSING

What you need to know

The world of copyright and licensing can seem very daunting, particularly because there is an obligation on schools to comply with copyright law. We're here to help you through the process and to keep you legal. The guidelines below explain the most common copyright and licensing issues.

Singing Songs in the Classroom

You are free to use all of the material for teaching purposes within the classroom. If photocopying any part of the book for teaching purposes please report this usage, when requested, to CLA and PMLL (or similar copy licensing agencies in your territory) to ensure that you are legally protected.

Singing Songs in an Assembly or in Church

Songs may be sung in assembly without charge. However, the reproduction of the lyrics and/or musical scores for use in an assembly or a church requires a licence. The following licences from Christian Copyright Licensing Limited (www.ccli. com) permit the photocopying or reproduction of song lyrics or musical scores – for example to create song sheets or to display the lyrics or music using any electronic display medium:

For UK schools: A Collective Worship Copyright Licence (CWCL) and a Collective Worship Music Reproduction Licence (CWMRL)

For churches: A Church Copyright Licence (CCL) and a Music Reproduction Licence (MRL)

The following credit should be included with the lyrics:
'Reproduced by kind permission © Out of the Ark Ltd'

Please ensure that you log the songs that are used on your CWCL and CWMRL copy report.

Your CWCL licence also grants you permission to display the song lyrics from our Words on Screen™ CD ROMs using any electronic display medium including touchscreens and whiteboards. Simply log the song titles on your copy report.

Organisations that do not hold one of the above licences should contact Out of the Ark Limited directly for permission.

Helpful information can be found on the following website:

A Guide to Licensing Copyright in Schools:
www.outoftheark.com/licensing

And remember, we are always happy to help. For advice simply contact our customer services team:

Tel: **+44 (0)20 8481 7200**   Email: **copyright@outoftheark.com**

Singing Songs in a Concert

If you are performing any of our songs for the public on school premises (i.e. to anyone other than pupils or staff) then royalty payments become due. Contact Out of the Ark Music directly to obtain a licence. **Please note:** There is no need to obtain a licence from the publisher if your school has a **Performing Rights Society (PRS)** licence.

If you are performing songs at a public venue (other than on the school premises or in a church) then the performance should be logged on the venue's PRS report.

If photocopying or reproducing song lyrics or musical scores for use in concerts – for example to create song sheets, or to display the lyrics or music using any electronic display medium – please report this usage, when requested, to CLA and PMLL (or similar copy licensing agencies in your territory) to ensure that you are legally protected.

Making an Audio Recording or a Video of the Performance

If you wish to make an audio or video recording of your performance of any of our works and to produce copies please contact Out of the Ark Music's Customer Services team on 020 8481 7200 for further information on obtaining the relevant licence from MCPS. Alternatively you can contact MPCS directly and they will issue the relevant licence on our behalf:

www.prsformusic.com

Use of Audio CDs and Digital Media (including Copying and File-sharing)

The content of Audio CDs and CD ROMs may be played directly from the disc anywhere on a school's premises.

Copying, installation and file sharing of any digital media from Out of the Ark Music are strictly forbidden without a licence from the publisher. This restriction includes all software regardless of whether it was supplied via audio CD, CD ROM, download, streaming or any other means.

Out of the Ark Music can provide schools with a **Digital Site Licence** which grants a number of file copying and file sharing rights enabling software to be used in multiple locations within the school.

Out of the Ark's **Words on Screen™** products are supplied with a **Single User Licence** which grants a number of rights to the purchaser including limited installation, downloading and streaming rights.

The **S!ng** Series

A fabulous new series designed to **get your school singing** about almost anything and everything! Each book contains ideas and tips on how to get going, a few **vocal warm-ups** to prepare your voices and **a whole mixture of irresistibly singable songs**, that include harmonies, rounds and group-singing opportunities!

S!ng Something SILLY!

A fantastic collection of crazy, dotty, loopy and potty songs to sing for the fun of it!

S!ng Together

A fabulously harmonious collection of songs – ideal for assemblies, choirs and happy singing!

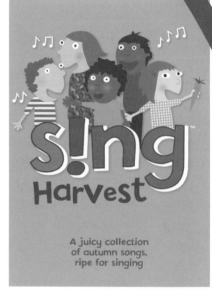

S!ng Harvest

A juicy collection of autumn songs, ripe for singing

Let yourselves go with this wild and wacky collection, jam-packed with the nonsensical, the ridiculous and the utterly hilarious! Whether you want a little light relief during a busy day, or you're looking for songs for a show-stopping performance, sing your way through this mad mixture of very silly songs, perfect for any time of the year.

From *One Little Voice* to the idea that *We're Better Together*, this collection of songs cleverly combines the themes of unity, belonging, friendship and respect with the feel-good factor that only singing can bring.

This collection of harvest songs includes everything from giving thanks and sowing seeds to harvest celebrations and juicy fruit. There's a lively dance for making bread and even a bunch of singing vegetables!

Spring is definitely in the air with this Easter collection, which is not only bursting with songs about chocolate, Easter bunnies and new life, but also offers more thought-provoking songs that cleverly unpack the Easter story. S!ng, s!ng, s!ng your way to Easter with this fantastic variety of springtime treats.

S!ng Easter

A dynamic collection of Easter songs, full of joy and bursting with life

Out of the Ark Music

Kingsway Business Park, Oldfield Road, Hampton, Middlesex TW12 2HD, UK
Tel: +44 (0)20 8481 7200 Fax: +44 (0)20 8941 5548
Email: info@outoftheark.com   www.outoftheark.com